I Love You 10!
~Love That Counts~

Written &
Illustrated
by

Ruth Baird

Publication Notes:

I Love You 10! ~ Love That Counts"
Text and Illustration Copyright © 2023 1-12608926751
Library of Congress Catalogue Number 2023910704
ISBN: 978-1-961517-00-4 (paperback) 978-1-961517-01-1
(hardcover) 978-1-961517-03-5 (ebook) 978-1-961517-02-8 (español)
978-1-961517-04-2 (español libro electronico)

Published by Dandelion Seed Entertainment.
DandelionSeedEntertainment.com.

Book design, written, and Illustrated by Ruth Baird
RuthBushmanBaird.com
Summary: A child tries to count 10 kinds of love at a family party.
1. Juvenile Fiction Counting & Numbers.
2. Juvenile Fiction Family & Multigenerational.
3. Juvenile Fiction Friendship.
First Edition

Dedication:

I once knew a little child
who held up ten little fingers and exclaimed,
"I love you ten!" Ten was the biggest number
in the child's world. I shared that story with
my own children. We often repeated that
phrase to say I love you.

This book is dedicated to my husband,
children and grandchildren:
David, Daniel, Rebecca, Michael,
Rachel, Anna, Elisabeth, Sarah, Joshua,
Kayla, David, Jason, Elijah, and Lily
"I Love you 10!"

Look!
I can count to ten
on my fingers.

1, 2, 3, 4, 5,
6, 7, 8, 9, 10.

I love you ten!

Today is the family party.
Do you think I can count
ten kinds of love before night comes?

Let's try!

1 ~ Creator Love

I think I found the first love already.
I hear Mami pray and say
"love" and "Thank you".
When we pray, I feel warm inside.

2 ~ Romantic Love

I see Mami and Papi kiss.
They say they love each other.
It makes me smile.
That's a second
kind of love.

3 ~ Parent Love

Ouch!
I tripped over Puppy!

Mami and Papi give me hugs and
help me feel better. Parents are my third love.

4 ~ Sister & Brother Love

I play with my twin sister and brother.
Even if they knock my blocks
or pull my hair, I love them,
and they love me.
I already have four loves!

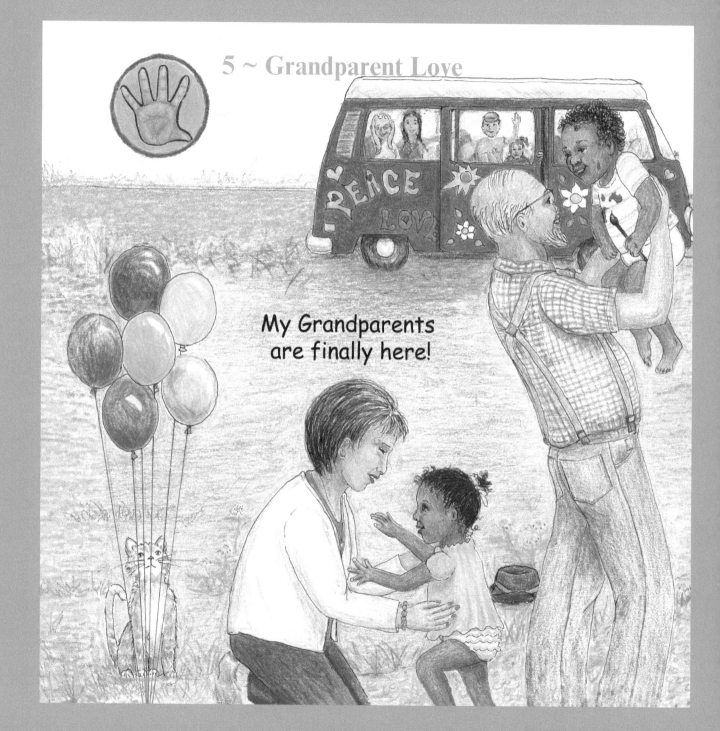

My Grandparents
are finally here!

They call me "Dearest heart"
and "Honey".
I love them to the
moon and back.
Wow, I've counted
five loves!

6 ~ Aunts, Uncles & Cousins Love

Uh-oh.
The family is all here.
Maybe there's no more love that counts...

7 ~ Friend Love

Hooray!
There's more love to count.
Here come Mary and Jon.
My friends
are the seventh love!

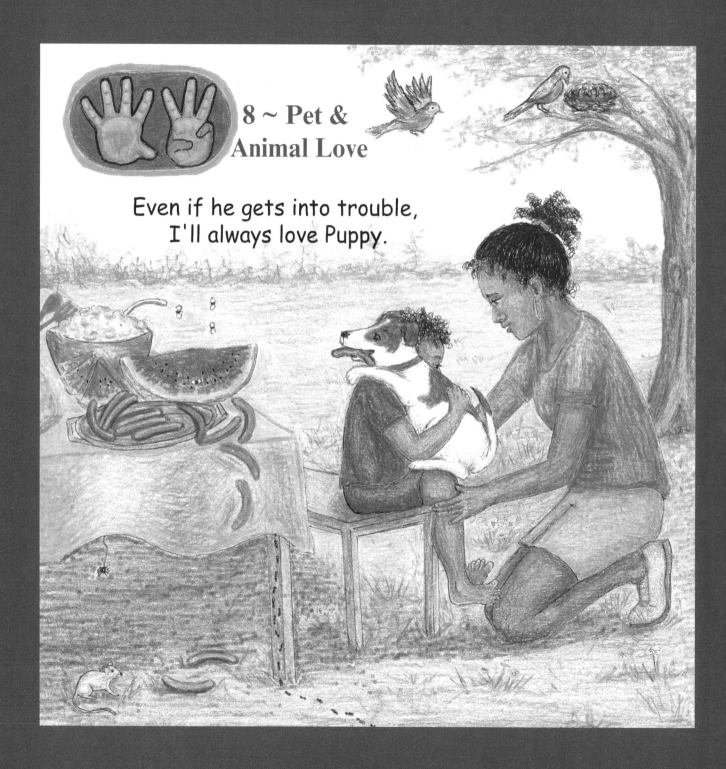

8 ~ Pet &
Animal Love

Even if he gets into trouble,
I'll always love Puppy.

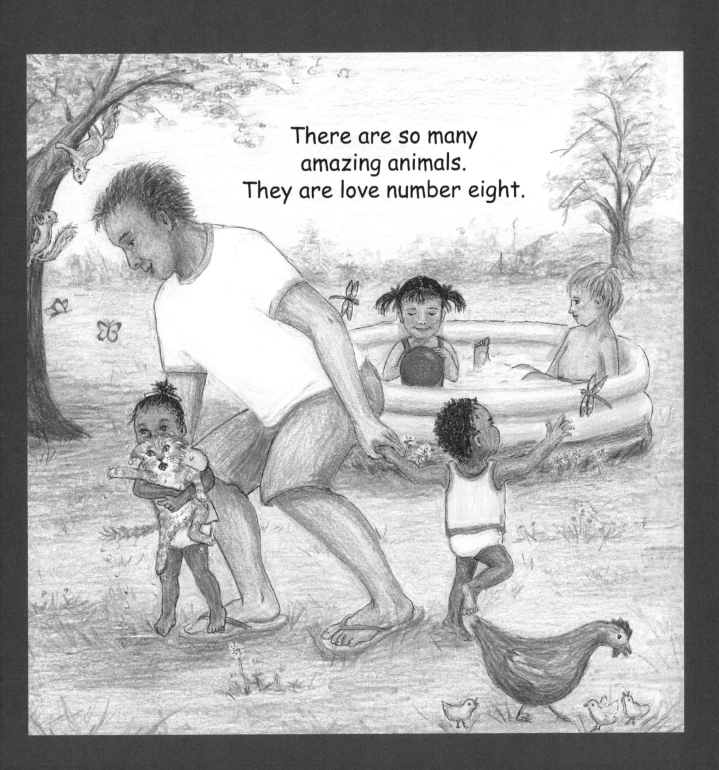

There are so many
amazing animals.
They are love number eight.

Love number nine is easy. Look at the wonderful trees and Flowers. I love the Sun, Moon, and Stars.

9 ~ Nature Love

I also love the Mountains, Wind
and Rivers that make
this world so beautiful.
I'm very thankful for the Earth.

~ Together we sing under the stars

Is it okay I didn't
find ten kinds of love?

songs of love and peace~

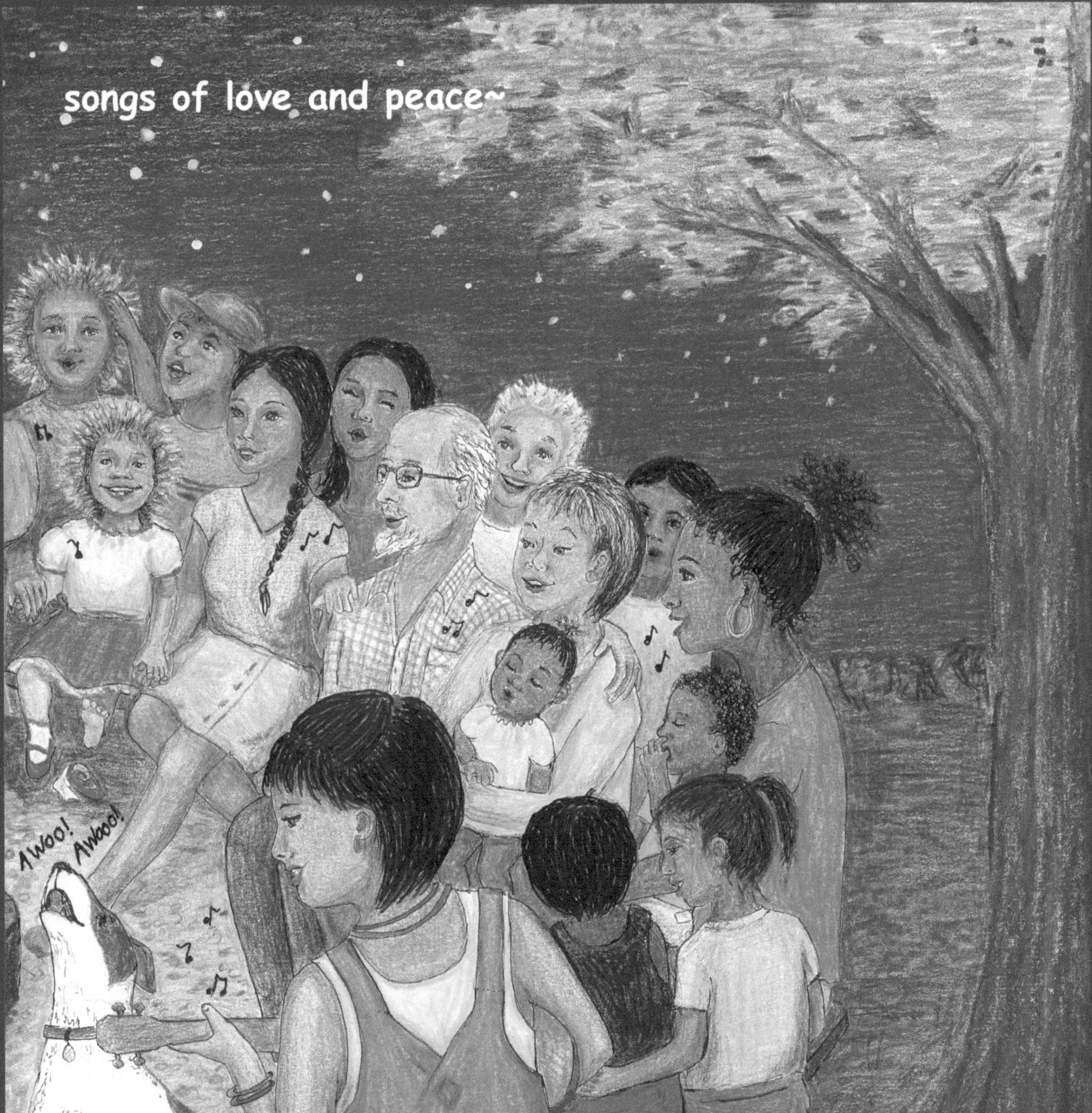

I think I know the tenth love.

I Love me!

1. Creator Love

10. Self Love!

2. Romantic Love

4. Sister & Brother Love

3. Parent Love

5. Grandparent Love

6. Aunts, Uncles & Cousins Love

9. Nature Love

7. Friend Love

8. Pets & Animal Love

You did it!
You counted
ten loves.
Goodnight,
dear. We
love you ten
-and more.

Fun Things to Talk About

1. What are your favorite kinds of love?

2. What would you name the child in the story?

3. What would you name Sister and Brother twins? How many times did brother twin get his shirt dirty?

4. What activity in the story would you like to do?

5. Some families look alike. Some don't. This family has a Latina grandma, an African grandpa, an Asian grandma, and a European grandpa. How is your family the same? How is it different?

6. Do you have pets? What are your favorite kinds of animals? Are the dog and cat on every page?

7. Is there a limit of people you can love?

8. Who are the people in your life that teach you about love?

9. What loves would you count on your toes?*

10. What are your favorite colors? Can you find these colors?

Pink, Red, Orange, Yellow, Green, Turquoise, Blue, Indigo, Purple

*Ruth's Website : RuthBushmanBaird.com

Printed in the USA
CPSIA information can be obtained
at www.ICGtesting.com
LVHW070106260823
755613LV00005B/47